This Book Belongs To:

COPYRIGHT © 2004 Nanci Bell
Gander Publishing
450 Front Street
Avila Beach, CA 93424
805-541-5523 • 800-554-1819

VISUALIZING AND VERBALIZING AND V/V ARE
REGISTERED TRADEMARKS OF NANCI BELL.

14   13   12   11   5   6   7   8

ISBN 0-945856-39-3   978-0-945856-39-9

Overview and Directions

This workbook is offered to provide a wider selection of material for practice developing gestalt imagery and language comprehension with the *Visualizing and Verbalizing for Language Comprehension and Thinking*® (V/V®) program.

Following the steps of V/V®, detail and gestalt imagery are developed with Sentence by Sentence, Multiple Sentence, Whole Paragraph, and Paragraph by Paragraph V/V® stimulation.

The V/V® workbooks contain high-imagery stories and the following workbook activities:

- Imagery questions
- Picture summary exercises
- Word summary prompts
- Page summary prompts
- Main idea exercises
- Higher order thinking (HOT) questions
- Paragraph writing prompts

Before the student begins each story, he/she should decode each vocabulary word and visualize the meaning. This will help create imagery and develop contextual fluency. When answering imagery questions, the student may write phrases or partial sentences to describe his/her imagery.

These workbooks have been written specifically to help students learn and discover the wonder of the written word by improving gestalt imagery, critical thinking, and writing skills. Once these skills are developed, the possibilities are endless.

Remember, you can help students do this. You can do anything!

Nanci Bell
2004

There are three workbooks at each reading level:

Book A • Sentence by Sentence
Book B • Sentence by Sentence and Multiple Sentence
Book C • Multiple Sentence, Whole Paragraph, and Paragraph by Paragraph

Meet Ivan!

I am Ivan, King of the Neighborhood. I'm big and wide and full of pride!

I **love** to eat!

I **love** to sleep!

I am a cat!

1 Life in Space

Two astronauts live high above the Earth in the International Space Station. The station is about the size of a three-bedroom house. The astronauts are often alone there for months at a time. But they are not bored. They are busy doing experiments. They can even send email to their friends and family. Then, after six months in space, a new crew takes their place and they can go home.

Vocabulary:

astronaut: a person whose job it is to fly to and work in space

International Space Station: a large spacecraft built by 15 countries that orbits around the Earth

astronaut: a person whose job it is to fly to and work in space

experiments: tests that are done to learn if an idea is true

---

1 **First and Second Sentences:** Two astronauts live high above the Earth in the International Space Station. The station is about the size of a three-bedroom house.

What did those words make you picture?_____

_____

_____

1. What did you see for the astronauts?_____

_____

2. What did you see for the International Space Station?_____

_____

3. What did you picture for the size of the station?_____

_____

4. Where did you see the station in the sky?_____

_____

2 **Third, Fourth, and Fifth Sentences:** The astronauts are often alone there for months at a time. But they are not bored. They are busy doing experiments.

What did those words make you picture?_____

_____

_____

1. How did you see the astronauts being alone?_____

_____

2. What did you picture for how long they might be alone?_____

_____

3. What did you see for the experiments?_____

_____

4. What did you see them doing when they did the experiments?____

_____

3 **Sixth and Seventh Sentences:** They can even send email to their friends and family. Then, after six months in space, a new crew takes their place and they can go home.

What did those words make you picture? _____

_____

_____

1. How did you see them sending email? _____

_____

2. What did you see for their friends and family getting the email? _____

_____

3. What did you see for the new crew? _____

_____

4. What did you see for the astronauts going home? _____

_____

Picture Summary:

Number your images in order.

[ ] The astronauts do experiments up in the space station.

[ ] The astronauts can send email to their friends and family.

[ ] After six months, the two astronauts go home and a new crew takes their place.

[ ] Two astronauts live high above the Earth in the small International Space Station.

Write a Word Summary:

_____

_____

_____

_____

_____

_____

Main Idea:

Check the box that best describes all your images—the main idea.

☐ Astronauts spend six months living and doing experiments aboard the International Space Station.

☐ After six months, a new crew of astronauts fly to the Space Station and the old crew goes home.

☐ The International Space Station is about the size of a three-bedroom house.

HOT Questions:

1. Why do you think we have an International Space Station? _____

_____

2. Why do you think it is called international? _____

_____

3. Do you think astronauts from a lot of countries might go to the station? _____

_____

4. Why do you think only two astronauts are at the station at one time? _____

_____

5. Why do you think a new crew takes their place after six months? Why not after a year? ___

_____

6. What do you think the experiments might be? _____

_____

7. What do you think we could learn from these experiments and who might the knowledge help? ___

_____

Make up a story about being an astronaut.

_____

_____

_____

_____

_____

_____

_____

_____

_____

_____

_____

_____

_____

Did you use all of the Structure Words? Check each one you used.

| ☐ What | ☐ Size | ☐ Color | ☐ Number | ☐ Shape | ☐ Where |
| ☐ Movement | ☐ Mood | ☐ Background | ☐ Perspective | ☐ When | ☐ Sound |

2 The Storm Chaser

Warren Faidley is famous for chasing storms and taking pictures for magazines. He travels across the U.S. in his van looking for large storms. He checks the weather radar from inside his van and races down small roads toward a storm. As the winds begin to swirl around in strong gusts, Warren looks in the sky. Then, near the back edge of a storm, a tornado appears. Warren stops the van, takes out his camera, and begins to shoot.

Vocabulary:

radar: a system that uses radio waves to check the distance and speed of a storm
swirl: to move around quickly; to spin
tornado: a dangerous funnel-shaped cloud that moves on the ground and destroys everything in its path

---

1 **First and Second Sentences:** Warren Faidley is famous for chasing storms and taking pictures for magazines. He travels across the U.S. in his van looking for large storms.

What did those words make you picture?_____

_____

_____

1. What did you picture for Warren?_____

   _____

2. What did you see for him "chasing storms"?_____

   _____

3. How did you see him traveling across the U.S.?_____

   _____

4. What did you see for large storms?_____

---

2 **Third and Fourth Sentences:** He checks the weather radar from inside his van and races down small roads toward a storm. As the winds begin to swirl around in strong gusts, Warren looks in the sky.

What did those words make you picture?_____

_____

_____

1. How did you see him checking the weather radar?_____

   _____

2. What did you see for him driving on small roads?_____

   _____

3. What did you see for the wind?_____

   _____

4. What did you see him doing in strong winds?_____

   _____

3 **Fifth and Sixth Sentences:** Then, near the back edge of a storm, a tornado appears. Warren stops the van, takes out his camera, and begins to shoot.

What did those words make you picture?_____

_____

1. What did you see for a tornado?_____

_____

2. What did you see Warren doing when he saw the tornado?_____

_____

3. What did you see for his camera?_____

_____

4. What did you picture him shooting?_____

_____

Picture Summary:

Number these in order.

☐ Warren stops his van, takes out his camera, and begins to shoot pictures.

☐ Warren travels across the U.S. looking for large storms to photograph.

☐ Near the back edge of a storm, a tornado appears.

☐ He checks the weather radar and watches for swirling winds.

Write a Word Summary:

_____

_____

_____

_____

_____

_____

Critical Thinking

Main Idea:

Check the box that best describes all your images—the main idea.

☐ Warren Faidley looks in the sky as the winds begin to swirl in strong gusts.

☐ Warren Faidley travels across the U.S. to find and take pictures of storms.

☐ Warren Faidley checks the weather radar and races his van toward the storm.

HOT Questions:

1. Why do you think Warren looks for storms?_____

_____

2. Why do you think Warren travels across the United States instead of staying in one place and waiting for a storm to come?_____

_____

3. Why do you think Warren has a weather radar in his van?_____

_____

4. Why do you think Warren races down small roads and not city streets?_____

_____

5. Why do you think Warren stopped the van?_____

_____

6. Why do you think strong winds were a signal for him to look in the sky?_____

_____

7. Why do you think Warren began to take pictures? _____

_____

Make up an exciting story about chasing a storm that becomes a tornado!

_____

_____

_____

_____

_____

_____

_____

_____

_____

_____

_____

_____

_____

_____

Did you use all of the Structure Words? Check each one you used.

| ☐ What | ☐ Size | ☐ Color | ☐ Number | ☐ Shape | ☐ Where |
| ☐ Movement | ☐ Mood | ☐ Background | ☐ Perspective | ☐ When | ☐ Sound |

3 Venice

In Venice, Italy, the people use boats instead of cars. The city was built on 120 small islands, so it has canals instead of streets. When a person wants to go across town, they hire a fast water taxi to take them. They can walk from island to island using some of the 400 bridges. But most tourists want to ride the long boats called gondolas. They relax in these slow boats and enjoy the lovely sights.

Vocabulary:

canal: a waterway that was built for boats
water taxi: a boat with a motor
gondola: a type of long narrow boat that is used in Venice

---

1 **First and Second Sentences:** In Venice, Italy, the people use boats instead of cars. The city was built on 120 small islands, so it has canals instead of streets.

What did those words make you picture?_____

_____

_____

1. What do you see for Venice?_____

_____

2. What did you see for people using boats?_____

_____

3. What did you see for the canals?_____

_____

4. What did you see for the 120 small islands?_____

_____

2 **Third and Fourth Sentences:** When a person wants to go across town, they hire a fast water taxi to take them. They can walk from island to island using some of the 400 bridges.

What did those words make you picture?_____

_____

_____

1. What did you see for a person going across town?_____

_____

2. What did you see for the water taxi?_____

_____

3. What did you see for the bridges?_____

_____

4. How many bridges did you picture?_____

_____

3 **Fifth and Sixth Sentences:** But most tourists want to ride the long boats called gondolas. They relax in these slow boats and enjoy the lovely sights.

What did those words make you picture?_____

_____

_____

1. What did you see for the gondolas?_____

_____

2. What colors did you picture for the gondolas?_____

_____

3. How did you see the gondola moving through the water?_____

_____

4. What did you see for tourists relaxing on the gondolas?_____

_____

Picture Summary:

Number your images in order.

People in Venice use boats instead of cars, because they have canals instead of streets.

Tourists like to ride down the canals in the long boats called gondolas.

They can also walk from island to island using some of the 400 bridges.

When a person wants to go across town, they hire a fast water taxi to take them.

Write a Word Summary:

_____

_____

_____

_____

_____

_____

Critical Thinking

Main Idea:

Check the box that best describes all your images—the main idea.

☐ Most tourists in Venice, Italy want to ride the long boats called gondolas.

☐ People hire fast water taxis to take them across Venice, Italy.

☐ Venice, Italy is an island city with canals and boats instead of streets and cars.

HOT Questions:

1. Why do you think the people of Venice use boats instead of cars?_____
_____

2. Why do you think the city has canals rather than streets?_____
_____

3. How did the fact that the city sits on 120 islands affect how it was built?_____
_____

4. Why do you think the city needs to have so many bridges?_____
_____

5. Why do you think a person might need a water taxi?_____
_____

6. Do you think this city is unusual? Why or why not?_____
_____

7. Why do you think the tourists like to ride the gondolas?_____
_____

Make up a story about solving a mystery while you were exploring Venice.

_____

_____

_____

_____

_____

_____

_____

_____

_____

_____

_____

_____

_____

_____

_____

Did you use all of the Structure Words? Check each one you used.

☐ What   ☐ Size   ☐ Color   ☐ Number   ☐ Shape   ☐ Where

☐ Movement   ☐ Mood   ☐ Background   ☐ Perspective   ☐ When   ☐ Sound

4 The Iditarod Sled Dog Race

Susan Butcher stood on the sled as her team of Huskies raced across snowy Alaska in the Iditarod Race. At the first checkpoint, Susan jumped off the dogsled to care for her furry dogs. She made a nice soft bed of warm straw for the dogs to rest on. Then she gave them big bowls of food and water. While the dogs ate, Susan took off their booties. She had to check their paws for any sign of injury. Then Susan ate and took a short nap. Soon she and her dog team were flying down the trail again toward their next win.

Vocabulary:

Susan Butcher: a four-time winner of the Iditarod Race

Huskies: a type of dog that is very strong

Iditarod Race: an annual event in which teams of dog sleds race 1100 miles across Alaska from Anchorage to Nome

checkpoint: a place where the teams stop and rest during the race

booties: small soft warm boots

1 **First and Second Sentences:** Susan Butcher stood on the sled as her team of Huskies raced across snowy Alaska in the Iditarod Race. At the first checkpoint, Susan jumped off the dogsled to care for her furry dogs.

What did those words make you picture?_____

_____

1. What did you see for snowy Alaska?_____

_____

2. What did you see for the Huskies?_____

_____

3. What did you see for Susan's dogsled?_____

_____

4. What did you see for her caring for her dogs?_____

_____

2 **Third and Fourth Sentences:** She made a nice soft bed of warm straw for the dogs to rest on. Then she gave them big bowls of food and water.

What did those words make you picture?_____

_____

1. What did you see for the straw?_____

_____

2. What did you see for the dogs resting?_____

_____

3. What did you picture for the bowls?_____

_____

4. What did you hear?_____

_____

3 **Fifth and Sixth Sentences:** While the dogs ate, Susan took off their booties. She had to check their paws for any sign of injury.

What did those words make you picture?_____

_____

_____

1. What did you see for the dogs eating?_____

2. What did you see for the booties?_____

3. Did you picture the dog's paws as being big or small?_____

4. How did you see Susan checking their paws?_____

4 **Seventh and Eighth Sentences:** Then Susan ate and took a short nap. Soon she and her dog team were flying down the trail again toward their next win.

What did those words make you picture?_____

_____

_____

1. What did you see for Susan eating?_____

2. Where did you see Susan taking her nap?_____

3. What did you see for them back on the trail?_____

4. How did you see the trail?_____

Picture Summary:

Number your images in order.

[ ] Susan stood on the sled as the dogs raced.

[ ] Susan removed the dogs' booties and carefully checked their paws.

[ ] Susan stopped at the checkpoint to rest and eat.

[ ] Susan and the dogs raced back down the trail.

Write a Word Summary:

_____

_____

_____

_____

_____

_____

Critical Thinking

Main Idea:

Check the box that best describes all your images—the main idea.

☐ Susan Butcher gave her dogs big bowls of food and water at the checkpoint.

☐ Susan Butcher ate and took a short nap after making sure her dogs were comfortable.

☐ At the checkpoint, Susan Butcher took care of her dogs and rested before they continued to race down the trail.

HOT Questions:

1. Why do you think there is a checkpoint in the race?_____

_____

2. Why do you think Susan made a soft warm bed for her dogs?_____

_____

3. Why do you think she used straw?_____

_____

4. Why do you think the dogs were wearing booties on their paws?_____

_____

5. Why do you think she had to check their paws for injury?_____

_____

6. Why do you think Susan took care of her dogs before she ate?_____

_____

7. Why do you think Susan only took a short nap?_____

_____

Make up an exciting story about racing in the Iditarod in the snowy wilds of Alaska.

Did you use all of the Structure Words? Check each one you used.

☐ What ☐ Size ☐ Color ☐ Number ☐ Shape ☐ Where
☐ Movement ☐ Mood ☐ Background ☐ Perspective ☐ When ☐ Sound

5 The Cursed Diamond

A blue stone the size of a clam, the Hope diamond is unusual. It was found in a mine in India in the 17th century. It has been passed down among rich people for hundreds of years. The blue color is due to traces of boron in the stone. But the gem glows red under certain light. The Hope diamond was first worn on a ribbon and then on a necklace with 61 white diamonds. Legend has it that the stone is cursed as many owners have had bad luck.

Vocabulary:

clam: a fist-sized creature that has a hard shell and lives in the sand
diamond: a gem that is very hard and very valuable
boron: a substance that is found in the Earth
gem: an expensive stone that is used in jewelry

---

1 **First and Second Sentences:** A blue stone the size of a clam, the Hope diamond is unusual. It was found in a mine in India in the 17th century.

What did those words make you picture?_____

_____

1. What color did you picture for the Hope diamond?_____

2. What size did you picture the diamond? _____

3. What did you see for a mine?_____

4. Were you picturing this from up close or from far away?_____

---

2 **Third and Fourth Sentences:** It has been passed down among rich people for hundreds of years. The blue color is due to traces of boron in the stone.

What did those words make you picture?_____

_____

1. What did you see for the rich people? _____

2. What did you see for "passing down"?_____

3. What did you see for hundreds of years? _____

4. Did you picture the blue as bright or dark? _____

3 **Fifth and Sixth Sentences:** But the gem glows red under certain light. The Hope diamond was first worn on a ribbon and then on a necklace with 61 white diamonds.

What did those words make you picture?_____

_____

_____

1. What color did you see it glowing?_____

_____

2. What did you see for the ribbon?_____

_____

3. What did you picture for a diamond necklace?_____

_____

4. How many white diamonds did you see on the necklace?_____

4 **Seventh Sentence:** Legend has it that the stone is cursed as many owners have had bad luck.

What did those words make you picture?_____

_____

_____

1. What did you see for the "legend"?_____

_____

2. What did you picture for the stone being cursed?_____

_____

3. What did you see for someone having bad luck?_____

_____

4. What sounds did you hear?_____

_____

Picture Summary:

Number your images in order.

☐ The Hope diamond is blue, but glows red under certain light because of the boron in it.

☐ Legend has it that the stone is cursed and has brought bad luck to many of its owners.

☐ The Hope diamond is a large diamond that was found in India in the 17th century.

☐ The Hope diamond has been passed down among rich people for hundreds of years.

Write a Word Summary:

_____

_____

_____

_____

_____

_____

Critical Thinking

Main Idea:

Check the box that best describes all your images—the main idea.

☐ A legend says the Hope diamond is cursed and gives its owners bad luck.

☐ The Hope diamond was found in India during the 17th century.

☐ The Hope diamond is a beautiful and unusual gem with a long history.

HOT Questions:

1. Why do you think the Hope diamond is considered unusual?_____

_____

2. Why do you think the diamond was found in a mine?_____

_____

3. Why do you think the diamond has been passed down among the rich?_____

_____

4. How do you think the diamond was "passed down"?_____

_____

5. Why do you think the diamond was placed on a necklace with white diamonds?_____

_____

6. Why do you think the diamond is considered cursed?_____

_____

7. Do you believe it is cursed? Explain._____

_____

Write a Story

Make up a story about anything you want!

Did you use all of the Structure Words? Check each one you used.

☐ What	☐ Size	☐ Color	☐ Number	☐ Shape	☐ Where
☐ Movement	☐ Mood	☐ Background	☐ Perspective	☐ When	☐ Sound

6 The Spirit Rover

In 2004, NASA sent the Spirit rover to land on Mars. The little car landed on the red ground after flying there in a rocket. Scientists on Earth drive the rover over the dirt by remote control. The robot car has arms to pick up dirt and rocks. The rover's camera sends back pictures showing lots of ground with nothing but rocks and dirt. The planet in these shots is hot and dry, with winds blowing around swirls of dust.

Vocabulary:

rover: a small vehicle that is used to explore the surface of a planet or moon
NASA: National Aeronautics and Space Agency; the American space program
scientists: people who study the world around us

1 **First and Second Sentences:** In 2004, NASA sent the Spirit rover to land on Mars. The little car landed on the red ground after flying there in a rocket.

What did those words make you picture?_____

_____

1. What did you picture for Mars?_____

2. What did you see for the Spirit rover?_____

3. What did you see for the rocket?_____

4. What did you see for the ground on Mars?_____

2 **Third and Fourth Sentences:** Scientists on Earth drive the rover over the dirt by remote control. The robot car has arms to pick up dirt and rocks.

What did those words make you picture?_____

_____

1. What did you see for the scientists?_____

2. How did you see them driving the car?_____

3. What did you see for the robot car's arms?_____

4. What did you see the arms picking up?_____

3 **Fifth and Sixth Sentences:** The rover's camera sends back pictures showing lots of ground with nothing but rocks and dirt. The planet in these shots is hot and dry, with winds blowing around swirls of dust.

What did those words make you picture?_____

_____

_____

1. What did you see for the rover's camera?_____

_____

2. What did you see for the pictures?_____

_____

3. What did you see for the planet being hot and dry?_____

_____

4. What did you see for the swirls of dust?_____

_____

Picture Summary:

Number your images in order.

 Scientists on Earth drive the rover by remote control.

 The Spirit rover landed on the red ground of Mars after flying there in a rocket.

 The planet is hot and dry, with winds blowing around swirls of dust.

 The rover's cameras send back shots of lots of ground, dirt, and rocks.

Write a Word Summary:

_____

_____

_____

_____

_____

_____

Critical Thinking

Main Idea:

Check the box that best describes all your images—the main idea.

☐ The Spirit rover travels over the ground on Mars and sends pictures back to scientists on Earth.

☐ The Spirit rover landed on the red ground after flying there in a rocket.

☐ The Spirit rover is a small robot car with arms to pick up dirt and rocks.

HOT Questions:

1. Why do you think NASA sent an unmanned robot to explore Mars?_____

_____

2. What would be some advantages of sending a robot? _____

_____

3. Why do you think the robot had to be sent in a rocket?_____

_____

4. Why do you think the Spirit rover is called a robot?_____

_____

5. Why do you think NASA named it Spirit?_____

_____

6. Why do you think the scientists wanted to know about Mars?_____

_____

7. What do you think might happen if we stopped exploring?_____

_____

Make up an exciting story about flying to Mars and driving the rover yourself.

_____

_____

_____

_____

_____

_____

_____

_____

_____

_____

_____

_____

Did you use all of the Structure Words? Check each one you used.

☐ What   ☐ Size   ☐ Color   ☐ Number   ☐ Shape   ☐ Where
☐ Movement   ☐ Mood   ☐ Background   ☐ Perspective   ☐ When   ☐ Sound

7 Titanic Disaster

The Titanic was a luxurious passenger ship that sank on its first trip. The owners thought the enormous ship would never sink, so it had only a few lifeboats. But on a cold night in 1912, with more than 2,000 men, women, and children aboard, the ship struck an iceberg. Water gushed into a hole on the side of the ship. Hundreds of passengers scrambled into the few lifeboats. They watched as the Titanic slid into the sea. Hours later, a large ship came and rescued the survivors.

Vocabulary:

Titanic: the name of a large luxury ship that sank in the Atlantic Ocean
luxurious: very expensive and high quality
lifeboats: small boats that are carried on a ship to save the passengers if the ship sinks
iceberg: a huge piece of ice that has broken off a glacier and is floating in an ocean

---

1 **First and Second Sentences:** The Titanic was an enormous passenger ship that sank on its first trip. The owners thought the luxurious ship would never sink, so it had only a few lifeboats.

What did those words make you picture?_____

_____

_____

1. What did you see for the Titanic?_____

_____

2. What size did you see for the ship?_____

_____

3. How did you see the ship being "luxurious"?_____

_____

4. What did you see for a few lifeboats? _____

---

2 **Third and Fourth Sentences:** But on a cold night in 1912, with more than 2,000 men, women, and children aboard, the ship struck an iceberg. Water gushed into a hole on the side of the ship.

What did those words make you picture?_____

_____

_____

1. What did you see for the men, women, and children on the ship?____

_____

2. What did you see for the iceberg?_____

_____

3. What did you hear when the ship hit the iceberg?_____

_____

4. How did you see the water gushing into the ship?_____

3 **Fifth, Sixth, and Seventh Sentences:** Hundreds of passengers scrambled into the few lifeboats. They watched as the Titanic slid into the sea. Hours later, a large ship came and rescued the survivors.

What did those words make you picture?_____

_____

_____

1. What did you see the passengers doing?_____

_____

2. What did you see for lots of people trying to get into a few lifeboats?

_____

3. How did you see the Titanic sliding below the sea?_____

_____

4. What did you see for the ship coming to rescue the survivors?_____

_____

Picture Summary:

Number your images in order.

[ ] The Titanic was a huge luxurious passenger ship that sank on its first trip.

[ ] Hundreds of passengers scrambled into the few lifeboats and watched as the Titanic sank.

[ ] On a cold night in 1912, with more than 2,000 men, women, and children aboard, the ship struck an iceberg.

[ ] A large ship came after a few hours and rescued the survivors.

Write a Word Summary:

_____

_____

_____

_____

_____

_____

Critical Thinking

Main Idea:

Check the box that best describes all your images—the main idea.

☐ The Titanic was a luxury ship filled with more than 2,000 passengers.

☐ Passengers on the Titanic scrambled to get into the few lifeboats.

☐ The Titanic was a luxury passenger ship that sunk when it struck an iceberg.

HOT Questions:

1. Why do you think the owners thought the Titanic would never sink?_____

_____

2. Why do you think the ship had only a few lifeboats?_____

_____

3. Why do you think the ship sank?_____

_____

4. What problems were caused by the ship having so few lifeboats and so many passengers?_____

_____

5. What problems do you think happened when the passengers tried to get in the lifeboats?_____

_____

6. How do you think more people might have been saved?_____

_____

7. What might have happened if the Titanic had never struck the iceberg?_____

_____

Make up a story about anything you want!

_____

_____

_____

_____

_____

_____

_____

_____

_____

_____

_____

_____

_____

_____

Did you use all of the Structure Words? Check each one you used.

| ☐ What | ☐ Size | ☐ Color | ☐ Number | ☐ Shape | ☐ Where |
| ☐ Movement | ☐ Mood | ☐ Background | ☐ Perspective | ☐ When | ☐ Sound |

8 The Taj Mahal

In 1630, the Shah of India built the Taj Mahal as a tomb for his wife. The Empress Mumtaz Mahal was the love of his life. She often helped the poor and was loved by the people. But she died young while she was traveling with the Shah. Sick with grief, he built the tomb as a monument to his eternal love for her. It took 22 years and thousands of workers to build the tomb. The building is spectacular and even has flowers made of jewels lining the marble walls. Surrounded by a lovely garden, it is one of the most magnificent buildings ever created.

Vocabulary:

Shah: a member of the royal family, like a king, that formerly ruled India
tomb: a place where a dead person is laid to rest
monument: a building or structure that is built to honor someone or something
magnificent: awesome; amazing

1 **First and Second Sentences:** In 1630, the Shah of India built the Taj Mahal as a tomb for his wife. The Empress Mumtaz Mahal was the love of his life.

What did those words make you picture?_____

_____

1. What did you picture for India?_____

2. What did you picture for the Shah?_____

3. What did you picture for his wife?_____

4. What did you see for her being the love of his life?_____

2 **Third and Fourth Sentences:** She often helped the poor and was loved by the people. But she died young while she was traveling with the Shah.

What did those words make you picture?_____

_____

1. What did you see for her giving him children?_____

2. What did you see for her being loved?_____

3. What did you picture for her dying?_____

4. What mood did you see for the Shah?_____

3 **Fifth and Sixth Sentences:** Sick with grief, he built the tomb as a monument to his eternal love for her. It took 22 years and thousands of workers to build the tomb.

What did those words make you picture?_____

_____

_____

1. How did you see the Shah being sick with grief?_____

_____

2. What did you picture for a monument?_____

_____

3. How did you see it taking 22 years to build?_____

_____

4. How did you see thousands of workers building the tomb?_____

_____

4 **Seventh and Eighth Sentences:** The building is spectacular and even has flowers made of jewels lining the marble walls. Surrounded by a lovely garden, it is one of the most magnificent buildings ever created.

What did those words make you picture?_____

_____

_____

1. What did you see for the flowers?_____

_____

2. How did you see marble walls?_____

_____

3. What did you see for the garden?_____

_____

4. How did you picture the building being "magnificent"?_____

_____

Picture Summary:

Number your images in order.

[ ] The Taj Mahal was built as a monument by the Shah of India for his wife after her death.

[ ] The Empress died while traveling with the Shah.

[ ] The Empress was loved by the people.

[ ] It took 22 years and thousands of workers to build the Taj Mahal.

Write a Word Summary:

_____

_____

_____

_____

_____

_____

Critical Thinking

Main Idea:

Check the box that best describes all your images—the main idea.

☐ The Taj Mahal took 22 years and thousands of workers to build.

☐ The Taj Mahal is a beautiful tomb that was built by the Shah of India as a monument to his wife.

☐ The Taj Mahal has walls that are lined with flowers made from jewels.

HOT Questions:

1. Why do you think the Shah built such a spectacular tomb?_____

_____

2. Why do you think the Empress was the love of his life?_____

_____

3. Why do you think the people loved the Empress so much?_____

_____

4. Do you think she wanted to be with him all the time? Explain. _____

_____

5. Do you think the Shah was sad for a long time after she died? Why or why not?_____

_____

6. Why do you think it took so many people so long to build the tomb?_____

_____

7. Do you think the Taj Mahal shows the Shah's love for his wife? Explain. _____

_____

Make up a story about visiting the Taj Mahal.

_____

_____

_____

_____

_____

_____

_____

_____

_____

_____

_____

_____

_____

_____

_____

Did you use all of the Structure Words? Check each one you used.

☐ What   ☐ Size   ☐ Color   ☐ Number   ☐ Shape   ☐ Where
☐ Movement   ☐ Mood   ☐ Background   ☐ Perspective   ☐ When   ☐ Sound

The Friendly Elephants

Elephants are very friendly and smart. They live as long as 70 years, and the females live in close-knit groups. They are playful, and are said to laugh. Elephants also cry when they are sad. When a friend who has been away returns, other elephants will spin around in a circle and trumpet. The whole herd acts as warm and loving parents to the calves.

Vocabulary:

close-knit: having close family ties
trumpet: to cry out loudly in celebration
calves: baby elephants

1 What did those words make you picture?_____

_____

1. What did you picture for elephants being playful?_____

_____

2. What did you picture for an elephant crying?_____

_____

3. What did you picture for an elephant seeing an old friend?_____

_____

4. What did you hear for the sound when an elephant trumpets?_____

_____

5. What did you picture for the herd acting as loving parents? _____

Critical Thinking

Write a Word Summary:

_____

_____

_____

_____

Main Idea:

Check the box that best describes all your images—the main idea.

☐ Elephants are warm and loving parents to a single calf.

☐ Elephants cry when they are sad or when one of them has died.

☐ Elephants are caring, friendly, and emotional animals with close family bonds.

HOT Questions:

1. Why do you think elephants are considered smart?_____

_____

2. How do you think elephants might be playful?_____

_____

3. What do you think might make an elephant laugh?_____

_____

4. How do you think you would know an elephant is laughing?_____

_____

5. Why do you think an elephant might cry?_____

_____

6. Would you like to see an elephant spin around and trumpet? Why or why not?_____

_____

10 Undercover Octopus

The Mimic octopus can change its color and shape to hide from her enemies. She can look like rocks, coral, sea snakes, and lionfish. She can disguise herself to sneak up on a fish she wants to eat. She lives mostly at the bottom areas of fresh water near the sea.

Vocabulary:

mimic: copy; imitate; look like
octopus: a sea animal that has eight arms
enemies: other animals that want to eat it
coral: a group of small sea animals that live together in large groups
lionfish: a type of colorful fish that has long poisonous spines
disguise: change her appearance

1

What did those words make you picture? _____

_____

1. What did you picture for the Mimic octopus? _____

_____

2. What did you picture for the octopus changing to look like rocks? _____

_____

3. What did you picture for her changing colors? _____

_____

4. What did you picture for her sneaking up on a fish? _____

_____

5. What did you picture for where the octopus lives? _____

_____

Critical Thinking

Write a Word Summary:

_____

_____

_____

_____

Main Idea:

Check the box that best describes all your images—the main idea.

☐ The Mimic octopus sneaks up on fish she wants to eat.

☐ The Mimic octopus lives mostly at the bottom areas of fresh water near the sea.

☐ The Mimic octopus changes her appearance to hide from or sneak up on animals and fish.

HOT Questions:

1. Why do you think the Mimic octopus would want to change her color?_____

_____

2. Why do you think changing her color could help the octopus avoid her enemies?_____

_____

3. Why do you think the octopus might want to look like a rock?_____

_____

4. Why do you think she might want to look like a sea snake or lionfish?_____

_____

5. Why do you think she sneaks up on a fish?_____

_____

6. Why do you think the Mimic octopus lives mostly at the bottom of the water?_____

11 Hairy Houdini

Ken Allen was a special orangutan at the San Diego Zoo. He was an escape artist. In the 1980s, Ken tricked his way out of his area again and again. The keepers called him "Hairy Houdini," after the famed escape artist. Ken would unscrew fence bolts, open doors, and climb the walls to get out of the zoo. Each time, his keepers would find him and put him back, but he never gave up.

Vocabulary:

orangutan: a type of ape with long arms and long red-brown hair

San Diego: a city in Southern California

escape artist: someone who is known for escaping from handcuffs, cages, etc.

Harry Houdini: a famous magician and escape artist who lived from 1876 to 1924

1 What did those words make you picture?_____

_____

1. What did you picture for Ken Allen?_____

_____

2. What did you picture for where he lived? _____

_____

3. What did you picture for his area in the zoo?_____

_____

4. What did you picture him doing to escape?_____

_____

5. How far did you picture Ken getting when he escaped?_____

_____

Critical Thinking

Write a Word Summary:

_____

_____

_____

_____

_____

Main Idea:

Check the box that best describes all your images—the main idea.

☐ Ken Allen was an orangutan that often escaped from the zoo.

☐ Ken Allen's keepers would find him and put him back.

☐ The keepers called the orangutan "Hairy Houdini" after the famed escape artist.

HOT Questions:

1. Why do you think Ken, the orangutan, was considered special?_____

_____

2. How do you think Ken learned to unscrew bolts?_____

_____

3. Why do you think the keepers called him "Hairy Houdini"?_____

_____

4. Why do you think Ken wanted to escape?_____

_____

5. How do you think the keepers could find him?_____

_____

6. Why do you think they were able to find him and put him back?_____

_____

12 The Fishing Fish

The anglerfish, who lives in the depths of the open sea, is a clever hunter. He lives in the pitch black of the deep water. He has a built-in fishing pole on his head and the tip glows in the darkness. He wiggles the glowing tip to attract little fishes for his dinner. Then he gobbles up the unsuspecting fish.

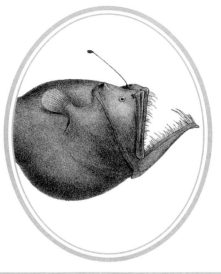

Vocabulary:

anglerfish: a small fish that lives deep in the ocean and has a glowing tip on its head to attract its prey
depths: the deepest part
clever: smart; intelligent
unsuspecting: not aware that something is wrong

1 What did those words make you picture?_____
_____

_____

1. Where did you picture the anglerfish living?_____

_____

2. What did you picture for the color of the deep water?_____

_____

3. What did you picture for the glowing tip on his head?_____

_____

4. What did you picture for the light in the depths of the water?_____

_____

5. What did you picture for how he attracts fish?_____

_____

Critical Thinking

Write a Word Summary:

_____

_____

_____

_____

_____

Main Idea:

Check the box that best describes all your images—the main idea.

☐ The anglerfish wiggles the glowing tip.

☐ The anglerfish has an unusual way to catch fish.

☐ The anglerfish lives in the pitch black of the deep water.

HOT Questions:

1. Why do you think the anglerfish is considered a clever hunter?_____

_____

2. Why do you think the water is pitch black where he lives?_____

_____

3. Why do you think he has a fishing pole on his head?_____

_____

4. Why do you think the tip glows?_____

_____

5. Why do you think he wiggles the tip to attract fish?_____

_____

6. Why do you think the fish are fooled into being eaten?_____

_____

13 The Moving Earth

Earthquakes happen when pieces of the crust of the Earth move and bump against one another. The big flat pieces are called tectonic plates, and there are many of them. Sometimes they push at each other, or one slips over or under another. Another cause for quakes is when hot liquid rock inside a volcano is sloshing about. This causes the ground to shake and roll. Quakes can make big cracks in the ground and can cause buildings to crumble.

Vocabulary:

earthquakes: a sudden strong shaking of the ground
crust: the hard outer part of the Earth
tectonic plates: huge thick sections of the Earth that move very slowly
sloshing: when a liquid splashes and moves around

1 What did those words make you picture?_____

_____

1. What did you picture for the crust of the Earth moving? _____

_____

2. What did you picture for a tectonic plate slipping over another plate?_____

_____

3. What did you picture for liquid rock?_____

_____

4. What did you picture for a volcano?_____

_____

5. What did you picture for cracks in the ground?_____

_____

Critical Thinking

Write a Word Summary:

_____

_____

_____

_____

_____

Main Idea:

Check the box that best describes all your images—the main idea.

☐ Volcanoes and the movement of tectonic plates cause earthquakes.

☐ The many big flat pieces of the Earth's crust are called tectonic plates.

☐ Earthquakes can cause buildings to crumble.

HOT Questions:

1. Why do you think the moving pieces of the Earth's crust bump into each other? _____

_____

2. Why do you think one plate might slip under or over another? _____

_____

3. Why do you think the plates might push at one another? _____

_____

4. Why do you think buildings might crumble in an earthquake? _____

_____

5. Why do you think people build buildings where an earthquake might happen? _____

_____

6. Would you like to feel an earthquake? Why or why not? _____

_____

14 Temper, Temper

With his poor vision and bad temper, the black rhino can be dangerous. Found in Africa, he is big and strong, and able to run very fast. He has a sharp horn on his snout that he uses to fight with other males over food. Unable to see far, he will charge at anything that scares him.

Vocabulary:

rhino: a rhinoceros; a large gray animal that lives in Africa
vision: the ability to see
snout: an animal's nose and mouth
charge: to run and attack something

1 What did those words make you picture?_____

_____

_____

1. What did you picture for how the rhino sees?_____

_____

2. What color and size did you picture the rhino?_____

_____

3. What did you see for the rhino running very fast?_____

_____

4. What did you picture for his horn and what did you see him doing with it?_____

_____

5. What did you see for him charging at anything that scares him? _____

_____

Critical Thinking

Write a Word Summary:

_____

_____

_____

_____

Main Idea:

Check the box that best describes all your images—the main idea.

☐ The black rhino has a sharp horn that he uses to fight with other males.

☐ The black rhino cannot see far, so he will charge at anything that scares him.

☐ With his bad temper, sharp horn, and poor vision, the black rhino is a dangerous animal.

HOT Questions:

1. Why do you think the black rhino can be dangerous? _____

_____

2. Why do you think poor vision would make the rhino dangerous? _____

_____

3. Why do you think the rhino has a horn on his snout? _____

_____

4. Why do you think the rhino fights with other males? _____

_____

5. Why do you think the rhino will charge at anything? _____

_____

6. How would you feel if you saw a rhino in the wild? _____

_____

15 Thomson's Gazelle

The Thomson's gazelle is one of the fastest runners in the world. The small animal uses its speed to escape from cheetahs on the plains of Africa. She also has great hearing and grazes in large groups. If she hears a cheetah, she will hop up and down on all four legs to warn the others. Then the herd runs, swerving this way and then the other, to lose the fast cat.

Vocabulary:

gazelle: a swift deer-like animal that lives in Asia and Africa
cheetahs: a large spotted cat; the cheetah is the fastest runner in the world
grazes: eats grass and other plants
swerving: turning quickly

1 What did those words make you picture? _____

_____

1. What did you picture for the Thomson's gazelle? _____

_____

2. What did you picture for her having great hearing? _____

_____

3. What did you picture for a large group of gazelles? _____

_____

4. What did you picture her doing to warn the herd? _____

_____

5. What did you picture the herd doing if there was a cheetah nearby? _____

Critical Thinking

Write a Word Summary:

_____

_____

_____

_____

Main Idea:

Check the box that best describes all your images—the main idea.

☐ The fast Thomson's gazelle has great hearing.

☐ The herd of Thomson's gazelles swerves this way and then the other.

☐ The Thomson's gazelle is very fast and has great hearing to help her escape from her enemy.

HOT Questions:

1. Why do you think the Thomson's gazelle needs to be a fast runner?_____

_____

2. Why do you think the gazelle needs to escape from the cheetah?_____

_____

3. Why do you think it is important for the gazelle to have great hearing?_____

_____

4. Why do you think the gazelle grazes in large groups?_____

_____

5. Why do you think the gazelle hops up and down as a warning signal?_____

_____

6. Why do you think the herd swerves this way and then the other when it runs?_____

_____

16

Glider of the Seas

The manta ray got its name from the Spanish word for blanket or cloak because he looks like one. His great gray fins stretch out to a length of almost two feet. He uses those fins to swim and he holds them still to glide through the water. Though he looks scary, the manta ray only eats tiny fish and animals that he scoops up into his big mouth.

Vocabulary:

manta ray: a large type of flat fish with a long thin tail
Spanish: the language spoken in Spain and many other countries
glide: to move easily through the water

---

1 What did those words make you picture?_____

_____

1. What did you picture for the manta ray?_____

_____

2. What did you picture that makes the manta ray look like a blanket or cloak?_____

_____

3. What color and size did you picture his fins?_____

_____

4. How did you picture the manta ray gliding through the water?_____

_____

5. What did you picture for how he gets his food? _____

Write a Word Summary:

_____

_____

_____

_____

_____

Main Idea:

Check the box that best describes all your images— the main idea.

☐ The manta ray has gray fins that stretch out to a length of almost two feet.

☐ The scary looking manta ray glides with his fins.

☐ The manta ray looks like a blanket and glides through the water eating small fish.

HOT Questions:

1. Why do you think the manta ray got its name from the Spanish word for blanket or cloak?_____

_____

2. How do you think the manta ray uses its long fins to move through the water?_____

_____

3. Why do you think the manta ray holds its fins still to glide through the water?_____

_____

4. Why do you think the manta ray might look scary to someone? _____

_____

5. Why do you think the manta ray is no danger to a swimmer?_____

_____

6. Why do you think he just scoops up the fish?_____

_____

17 Survivor

Steven Callahan, a young man, set sail on a warm tropical day from the Canary Islands in his small sailboat. Six days into his trip his boat sank in a sudden storm. Steven barely had time to get into his inflatable rubber life raft. He had grabbed a knife, sleeping bag, and supplies from his sinking boat.

Steven floated in the life raft on the open sea day after day . He had a spear gun and he was able to catch a fish or two. He was hungry, thirsty, and lonely. The sun beat down on his head. Sharks circled his raft.

Steven survived through violent storms that tossed his raft on the water. After over two months adrift, he spotted land. The island was made of jagged reefs and sharp cliffs. He could not get his raft to the land. Then he heard a boat motor. It was a fishing boat from the island. Steven was rescued after 76 days lost at sea.

Vocabulary:

Canary Islands: a group of islands off the coast of Africa

inflatable: able to be filled with air

life raft: a small boat that is used when a person's larger boat sinks

spear gun: a special gun that is used to shoot spears at fish (for spear fishing)

adrift: floating in the water without a sail, motor, or any way to steer

---

1 | **First Paragraph:** Steven Callahan, a young man, set sail on a warm tropical day from the Canary Islands in his small sailboat. Six days into his trip his boat sank in a sudden storm. Steven barely had time to get into his inflatable rubber life raft. He had grabbed a knife, sleeping bag, and supplies from his sinking boat.

What did those words make you picture?_____

_____

_____

1. What did you picture for Steven Callahan?_____

_____

2. What did you picture for the storm?_____

_____

3. What did you picture for his life raft?_____

_____

4. What did you picture Steven grabbing from his sinking boat?_____

2 **Second Paragraph:** Steven floated in the life raft on the open sea day after day. He had a spear gun and he was able to catch a fish or two. He was hungry, thirsty, and lonely. The sun beat down on his head. Sharks circled his raft.

What did those words make you picture?_____

_____

1. What did you picture for the open sea?_____

_____

2. What did you picture for Stephen in the life raft?_____

_____

3. What did you picture for what Steven was eating?_____

_____

4. What did you picture for the sharks circling his life raft?_____

_____

3 **Third Paragraph:** Steven survived through violent storms that tossed his raft on the water. After over two months adrift, he spotted land. The island was made of jagged reefs and sharp cliffs. He could not get his raft to the land. Then he heard a boat motor. It was a fishing boat from the island. Steven was rescued after 76 days lost at sea.

What did those words make you picture?_____

_____

1. What did you picture for the violent storms?_____

_____

2. What did you picture Steven doing during the storms?_____

_____

3. What did you picture for the island?_____

_____

4. What did you picture for Steven being rescued?_____

_____

Critical Thinking

Picture Summary:

Number these in order.

☐ Steven Callahan floated for over two months and then was rescued by a fishing boat.

☐ Steven Callahan's sailboat sank and left him stranded in a life raft on the open sea.

☐ Steven Callahan survived storms, thirst, and hunger while sharks circled his raft.

Main Idea:

Check the box that best describes all your images—the main idea.

☐ Steven Callahan survived for 76 days alone at sea in a life raft before he was rescued.

☐ Steven Callahan survived violent storms that tossed his life raft on the water.

☐ Steven Callahan had a spear gun and was able to catch a fish as he floated in the life raft.

HOT Questions:

1. Why do you think Steven set sail on a warm tropical day? _____

_____

2. Why do you think his sailboat sank? _____

_____

3. Why do you think Steven had a life raft made of rubber? _____

_____

4. Why do you think he grabbed supplies from his sinking boat? _____

_____

5. Why do you think it took so long for him to get to land? _____

_____

6. Why do you think sharks circled his life raft? _____

_____

Write a Word Summary about <u>Survivor</u>.

_____

_____

_____

_____

_____

_____

_____

_____

_____

_____

_____

_____

_____

_____

_____

Did you use all of the Structure Words? Check each one you used.

☐ What   ☐ Size   ☐ Color   ☐ Number   ☐ Shape   ☐ Where

☐ Movement   ☐ Mood   ☐ Background   ☐ Perspective   ☐ When   ☐ Sound

18 The Caterpillar

A caterpillar goes through many changes to become a butterfly. First, she crawls to the end of a leafy branch. The fat caterpillar makes a few threads and attaches herself to the branch. Then her skin begins to harden. Soon the hardened skin forms a shell around the body.

As the shell, or pupa, hardens in the sun, it protects the caterpillar as it starts to change. Long thin legs and brightly colored wings form inside. After a few weeks, a new butterfly is ready to come out.

The clear pupa starts to crack and split. The damp insect crawls out of her shell and into the warm sunlight. The butterfly wiggles its wings. They unfold and begin to dry. Then the butterfly flies away.

Vocabulary:

caterpillar: a worm-like creature that turns into a butterfly or moth
leafy branch: a branch with many leaves on it
pupa: a hard shell that surrounds and protects a caterpillar while it is becoming a butterfly

---

1 **First Paragraph:** A caterpillar goes through many changes to become a butterfly. First, she crawls to the end of a leafy branch. The fat caterpillar makes a few threads and attaches herself to the branch. Then her skin begins to harden. Soon the hardened skin forms a shell around the body.

What did those words make you picture? _____

_____

_____

1. What did you picture for a caterpillar? _____

_____

2. What did you picture for a butterfly? _____

_____

3. What did you see for the threads the caterpillar made? _____

_____

4. What did you see for the hardened skin? _____

_____

2 **Second Paragraph:** As the shell, or pupa, hardens in the sun, it protects the caterpillar as it starts to change. Long thin legs and brightly colored wings form inside. After a few weeks, a new butterfly is ready to come out.

What did those words make you picture?_____

_____

1. What did you picture for a pupa?_____

_____

2. What did you see for it hardening in the sun?_____

_____

3. What did you picture for the caterpillar changing inside the pupa?_____

_____

4. Where did you picture all this happening?_____

_____

3 **Third Paragraph:** The clear pupa starts to crack and split. The damp insect crawls out of her shell and into the warm sunlight. The butterfly wiggles its wings. They unfold and begin to dry. Then the butterfly flies away.

What did those words make you picture?_____

_____

1. What did you picture for the pupa starting to crack?_____

_____

2. How did you see the insect crawling out?_____

_____

3. What did you picture for her being damp?_____

_____

4. What color and shape did you picture the butterfly's wings?_____

_____

Critical Thinking

Picture Summary:

Number these in order.

☐ The caterpillar crawls to the end of a leafy branch and a shell forms around her.

☐ The pupa splits and a damp butterfly emerges, dries herself, and flies away.

☐ The shell, a pupa, protects the caterpillar while she grows long thin legs and colorful wings.

Main Idea:

Check the box that best describes all your images—the main idea.

☐ A caterpillar goes through many changes as she becomes a butterfly.

☐ Long thin legs and brightly colored wings form inside the pupa.

☐ The fat caterpillar makes a few threads and attaches herself to a leafy branch.

HOT Questions:

1. Why do you think it is important that the caterpillar can make thread?_____

_____

2. Why do you think the caterpillar attaches herself to the branch and doesn't just lie there?_____

_____

3. Why do you think the caterpillar needs a hard shell around her body?_____

_____

4. Why do you think it takes several weeks for the caterpillar to turn into a butterfly and not just a few minutes?_____

_____

5. Why do you think it might be good for the caterpillar to be fat?_____

_____

6. Why do you think the butterfly dries her wings before flying away?_____

_____

Write a Word Summary about <u>The Caterpillar</u>.

Did you use all of the Structure Words? Check each one you used.

☐ What	☐ Size	☐ Color	☐ Number	☐ Shape	☐ Where
☐ Movement	☐ Mood	☐ Background	☐ Perspective	☐ When	☐ Sound

19

A Living Dragon

The rare Komodo dragon is a lizard over ten feet long that lives on an island. He is green and grey with rough scaly skin. His tail is half of his total length and he has a long neck. The dragon has big sharp digging claws and 52 teeth made for tearing.

The dragon uses his long yellow tongue to taste the air. He finds deer, goats, pigs, and rats to eat. He sometimes digs his claws into the sand to find birds' eggs. He likes to lie in the sun to warm his body.

When he gets too warm, he can go for a swim. The Komodo dragon is a very good swimmer, using all four legs and steering with his strong tail to move through the ocean surf. Later he sleeps in a warm burrow that he digs in the ground. Able to live for up to 25 years, there is nothing on the island that can harm the Komodo dragon.

Vocabulary:

lizard: a type of reptile with a long scaly body, short legs, and a long tail
scaly skin: skin that is covered with small flat plates
burrow: a hole in the ground

---

1 | **First Paragraph:** The rare Komodo dragon is a lizard over ten feet long that lives on an island. He is green and grey with rough scaly skin. His tail is half of his total length and he has a long neck. The dragon has big sharp digging claws and 52 teeth made for tearing.

What did those words make you picture?_____

_____

_____

1. What did you picture for the Komodo dragon?_____

_____

2. What color and size did you picture the dragon?_____

_____

3. What did you picture for the dragon's tail?_____

_____

4. How did you picture his 52 teeth? _____

2 **Second Paragraph:** The dragon uses his long yellow tongue to taste the air. He finds deer, goats, pigs, and rats to eat. He sometimes digs his claws into the sand to find birds' eggs. He likes to lie in the sun to warm his body.

What did those words make you picture?_____

_____

1. What did you picture for his tongue?_____

_____

2. What did you picture the dragon doing with his tongue?_____

_____

3. What did you picture for him digging in the sand for eggs?_____

_____

4. How did you see him sunning his body? _____

_____

3 **Third Paragraph:** When he gets too warm, he can go for a swim. The Komodo dragon is a very good swimmer, using all four legs and steering with his strong tail to move through the ocean surf. Later he sleeps in a warm burrow that he digs in the ground. Able to live for up to 25 years, there is nothing on the island that can harm the Komodo dragon.

What did those words make you picture?_____

_____

1. What did you picture for the dragon swimming? _____

_____

2. What did you picture for the dragon steering with his tail? _____

_____

3. What did you picture for the dragon sleeping in a burrow?_____

_____

4. What did you picture that can harm the dragon?_____

_____

Critical Thinking

Picture Summary:

Number these in order.

[ ] The Komodo dragon is a strong swimmer, and can live up to 25 years.

[ ] The Komodo dragon is a long scaly lizard with sharp claws and teeth.

[ ] The Komodo dragon tastes the air to find animals to eat, and likes to lie in the sun.

HOT Questions:

1. Why do you think the Komodo dragon is called a dragon?_____

_____

2. How do you think the dragon uses his tongue to taste the air?_____

_____

3. Why do you think the size of his tail helps him swim?_____

_____

4. Why do you think his teeth are shapr and made for tearing?_____

_____

5. How do you think his scales might help him not be attacked by other animals?_____

_____

6. Why do you he sleeps in a burrow?_____

_____

Main Idea:

Check the box that best describes all your images—the main idea.

[ ] The Komodo dragon has a long neck and a tail that is over half of his total length.

[ ] The Komodo dragon uses his strong tail to move through the ocean surf.

[ ] The Komodo dragon is a large lizard with claws and sharp teeth that lives on an island.

Write a Word Summary about <u>The Living Dragon</u>.

_____

_____

_____

_____

_____

_____

_____

_____

_____

_____

_____

_____

_____

_____

_____

Did you use all of the Structure Words? Check each one you used.

☐ What	☐ Size	☐ Color	☐ Number	☐ Shape	☐ Where
☐ Movement	☐ Mood	☐ Background	☐ Perspective	☐ When	☐ Sound

20 Paricutin

In 1943, a Mexican farmer was busy plowing his cornfield. As he worked in the dusty field, he felt the ground rumble and shake. Then he saw a large crack in the ground. Curious, he walked closer and saw smoke rising from the hole. A strong smell of sulfur wafted through the air. Scared, the farmer ran home.

The next day the farmer returned to his field. But the crack was no longer there. Instead, a 30-foot high volcano was in the middle of the field. All day, rocks and ash came out of the volcano. By nightfall, the cone was over 150 feet high.

For nine years, the volcano erupted. It grew over 1,200 feet high. The lava it spewed covered the farmer's cornfield and two nearby villages. Then, just as suddenly as it was born, the volcano became quiet. The volcano became known as Paricutin.

Vocabulary:

curious: wanting to know about something
sulfur: a chemical that has a bad smel
wafted: flowed through the air
erupted: when lava explodes out of a volcano
lava: melted liquid rock that is very h
spewed: flowed out quickly

1 **First Paragraph:** In 1943, a Mexican farmer was busy plowing his cornfield. As he worked in the dusty field, he felt the ground rumble and shake. Then he saw a large crack in the ground. Curious, he walked closer and saw smoke rising from the hole. A strong smell of sulfur wafted through the air. Scared, the farmer ran home.

What did those words make you picture?_____

_____

_____

1. What did you picture for the Mexican farmer?_____

_____

2. What did you picture for him plowing his cornfield? _____

_____

3. How did you see the ground shaking?_____

_____

4. What did you see for the crack in the ground?_____

2 **Second Paragraph:** The next day the farmer returned to his field. But the crack was no longer there. Instead, a 30-foot high volcano was in the middle of the field. All day, rocks and ash came out of the volcano. By nightfall, the cone was over 150 feet high.

What did those words make you picture?_____

_____

1. What did you picture for the farmer going back to his field?_____

_____

2. What did you see for the volcano?_____

_____

3. What did you picture for the mood of the farmer when he saw the volcano instead of the crack?_____

_____

4. What did you picture for the rocks and ash coming out of the volcano? _____

_____

3 **Third Paragraph:** For nine years, the volcano erupted. It grew over 1,200 feet high. The lava it spewed covered the farmer's cornfield and two nearby villages. Then, just as suddenly as it was born, the volcano became quiet. The volcano became known as Paricutin.

What did those words make you picture?_____

_____

1. What did you picture for how long the volcano erupted?_____

_____

2. What did you see for the lava?_____

_____

3. What did you picture the lava doing?_____

_____

4. How did you picture the volcano quiet?_____

_____

Critical Thinking

Picture Summary:

Number these in order.

[ ] The farmer was in his cornfield when the ground shook and a crack appeared.

[ ] The volcano erupted for nine years, spewing lava and growing to over 1,200 feet high.

[ ] The next day, the volcano was 30 feet high and rocks and ash came out of it.

Main Idea:

Check the box that best describes all your images—the main idea.

[ ] The volcano spewed lava that covered the farmer's cornfield and two villages.

[ ] As a farmer worked in his cornfield in Mexico, the ground began to rumble and shake.

[ ] The Paricutin volcano erupted for nine years after suddenly beginning in a farmer's cornfield.

HOT Questions:

1. Why do you think the ground at the cornfield began to rumble and shake? _____

_____

2. Why do you think the farmer walked close to the crack in the ground? _____

_____

3. Why do you think the farmer ran home after seeing the crack? _____

_____

4. Why do you think the farmer returned the next day? _____

_____

5. What do you think the farmer did after the volcano erupted? _____

_____

6. How do you think the volcano affected the farmer and villages? _____

_____

Write a Word Summary about <u>Paricutin</u>.

_____

_____

_____

_____

_____

_____

_____

_____

_____

_____

_____

_____

_____

_____

Did you use all of the Structure Words? Check each one you used.

☐ What	☐ Size	☐ Color	☐ Number	☐ Shape	☐ Where
☐ Movement	☐ Mood	☐ Background	☐ Perspective	☐ When	☐ Sound

21

The Hippodrome

The Hippodrome was a racetrack set up for horses and chariots in ancient times. In the city of Constantinople, the track put on chariot races. Teams of four horses pulled the two-wheeled carts. The riders stood up and held the reins tightly as the horses dashed around the track.

The horses ran fast and wild. At any moment, a rider could be thrown to the ground and crushed under a wheel or horses' hooves. The chariots had to make seven laps around the dirt track. The crowds cheered to see the chariots rush toward the finish line, with dust flying, and riders yelling at their horses.

Vocabulary:

Hippodrome: a stadium where people watched chariot races
chariots: two-wheeled carts that were pulled by a team of horses
Constantinople: the eastern capital of the Roman Empire
ancient times: a long time ago (chariot races were held from about 400 B.C. until A.D. 500)

1 **First Paragraph:** The Hippodrome was a racetrack set up for horses and chariots in ancient times. In the city of Constantinople, the track put on chariot races. Teams of four horses pulled the two-wheeled carts. The riders stood up and held the reins tightly as the horses dashed around the track.

What did those words make you picture? _____

_____

1. What did you picture for the Hippodrome? _____

_____

2. What did you picture for a chariot race? _____

_____

3. How many horses did you picture pulling a chariot? _____

_____

4. What did you picture for the riders and what did you see them doing? _____

2 **Second Paragraph:** The horses ran fast and wild. At any moment, a rider could be thrown to the ground and crushed under a wheel or horses' hooves. The chariots had to make seven laps around the dirt track. The crowds cheered to see the chariots rush toward the finish line, with dust flying, and riders yelling at their horses.

What did those words make you picture? _____

_____

_____

1. What did you picture for the horses running fast and wild? _____

_____

2. What did you picture for the seven laps? _____

_____

3. What did you picture for the crowd cheering? _____

_____

4. Describe all your imagery for the chariots rushing to the finish line. _____

_____

Picture Summary:

Number these in order.

[ ] The crowds cheered to see the chariots rush toward the finish line.

[ ] The Hippodrome put on chariot races, with two-wheeled chariots and teams of four horses.

[ ] The chariots raced wildly around the dirt track to complete seven laps.

[ ] At any time, a rider could be thrown to the ground and crushed under a wheel or horses' hooves.

Write a Word Summary:

_____

_____

_____

_____

_____

Critical Thinking

Main Idea:

Check the box that best describes all your images—the main idea.

☐ Teams of four horses pulled two-wheeled carts called chariots around the racetrack.

☐ The Hippodrome was a popular place for people to watch dangerous chariot races.

☐ Crowds cheered to see the chariots rush toward the finish line.

HOT Questions:

1. Why do you think the Hippodrome was set up for chariot races?_____

_____

2. Why do you think the races had chariots and not cars or motorcycles?_____

_____

3. Why did they use horses instead of cars to pull the chariots?_____

_____

4. Why do you think the riders stood up and held on tight?_____

_____

5. What do you think might have happened to a rider if he fell?_____

_____

6. Do you think chariot racing was dangerous? Explain. _____

_____

7. Do you think chariot racing was exciting? Explain. _____

_____

Make up an exciting story about racing a chariot at the Hippodrome.

_____

_____

_____

_____

_____

_____

_____

_____

_____

_____

_____

_____

_____

Did you use all of the Structure Words? Check each one you used.

☐ What ☐ Size ☐ Color ☐ Number ☐ Shape ☐ Where
☐ Movement ☐ Mood ☐ Background ☐ Perspective ☐ When ☐ Sound

22 The Rain Forest

Rain forests are a small part of the Earth's surface, but half of all the plants and animals in the world live in them. The forests get plenty of sun, rain, and warm weather. So these forests are a great place for animals and plants to live.

The plants grow in several layers. Tall trees grow high into the sky with branches that reach out like an umbrella. This keeps most of the sunlight from reaching the forest floor. Other types of plants grow in the shade down below. All of these plants make oxygen. Because so many plants are in the rain forest, a large part of the world's oxygen is made there.

Animals and bugs move through each layer of the forest. Large animals and bugs roam on the forest floor. Monkeys, lizards, and bugs move through the trees. Birds and still more bugs fly around the treetops. There are often more kinds of butterflies in one square mile of rain forest than there are in the entire U.S.

Vocabulary:

rain forest: a forest that gets lots of heavy rain
oxygen: the gas in the air that people breathe to live; plants produce oxygen
one square mile: an area that is one mile long and one mile wide

---

1 **First Paragraph:** Rain forests are a small part of the Earth's surface, but half of all the plants and animals in the world live in them. The forests get plenty of sun, rain, and warm weather. So these forests are a great place for animals and plants to live.

What did those words make you picture? _____

_____

_____

1. What did you picture for the rain forest? _____

_____

2. What did you picture for how many plants and animals live in rain forests? _____

_____

3. What did you picture for the weather in the rain forest? _____

_____

4. What did you picture for plants and animals living in the rain forest? _____

2 **Second Paragraph:** The plants grow in several layers. Tall trees grow high into the sky with branches that reach out like an umbrella. This keeps most of the sunlight from reaching the forest floor. Other types of plants grow in the shade down below. All of these plants make oxygen. Because so many plants are in the rain forest, a large part of the world's oxygen is made there.

What did those words make you picture?_____

_____

1. What did you picture for the plants growing in layers?_____

_____

2. What did you picture for the umbrella branches of tall trees?_____

_____

3. What did you see for how much sunlight reached the forest floor?_____

_____

4. What did you picture for the plants on the forest floor?_____

_____

3 **Third Paragraph:** Animals and bugs move through each layer of the forest. Large animals and bugs roam on the forest floor. Monkeys, lizards, and bugs move through the trees. Birds and still more bugs fly around the treetops. There are often more kinds of butterflies in one square mile of rain forest than there are in the entire U.S.

What did those words make you picture?_____

_____

1. What did you picture for animals and bugs moving through the layers in the forest?_____

_____

2. What did you picture on the forest floor?_____

_____

3. What did you see in the trees?_____

_____

4. What did you see for more types of butterflies in one square mile compared to the entire U.S.? _____

_____

Critical Thinking

Picture Summary:

Number these in order.

☐ Each layer of the forest from the floor to the treetops has animals, bugs, and birds.

☐ Rain forests are a small part of the Earth's surface, but half of all the plants and animals live there.

☐ Tall trees grow high into the sky and spread out branches, shading the ground.

Main Idea:

Check the box that best describes all your images—the main idea.

☐ Animals and bugs move through each layer of the rain forest.

☐ A large part of the world's oxygen is made in the rain forests.

☐ Rain forests are a small but very important part of the Earth because many plants and animals live there.

HOT Questions:

1. Why do you think rain forests are home to so many different plants and animals?_____

_____

2. Why do you think a rain forest is a great place for plants and animals to live?_____

_____

3. How do the layers help rain forests be great places for plants and animals to live?_____

_____

4. Why do you think rain forests produce so much oxygen?_____

_____

5. Why might all the plants in a rain forest be important to the world?_____

_____

6. What do you think might happen to the world if the rain forests are destroyed?_____

_____

Write a Word Summary about <u>The Rain Forest</u>.

_____

_____

_____

_____

_____

_____

_____

_____

_____

_____

_____

_____

_____

_____

Did you use all of the Structure Words? Check each one you used.

| ☐ What | ☐ Size | ☐ Color | ☐ Number | ☐ Shape | ☐ Where |
| ☐ Movement | ☐ Mood | ☐ Background | ☐ Perspective | ☐ When | ☐ Sound |

23 Betsy Ross

Many believe that a young seamstress named Betsy Ross made the first American flag that had stars and stripes. Ross was a young widow when she took over her late husband's sewing business. She worked hard sewing clothes and flags for the navy.

The legend says that in 1776 George Washington came to Betsy's home. He asked her to make the new American flag. Together they worked on a design with stars and stripes. He wanted the stars to have six points, but Ross disagreed. She quickly showed him an easy way to make perfect stars with five points. Washington then agreed and the woman went to work.

Ross made a flag with 13 red and white stripes. In the corner was a blue square with a circle of 13 white stars in the middle. This flag is now known as the Betsy Ross flag. It became the official American flag in 1777.

Vocabulary:

seamstress: a woman whose job is to sew clothes and other items
widow: a woman whose husband has died
late husband: a husband who has died
official: approved by the government

---

1 **First Paragraph:** Many believe that a young seamstress named Betsy Ross made the first American flag that had stars and stripes. Ross was a young widow when she took over her late husband's sewing business. She worked hard sewing clothes and flags for the navy.

What did those words make you picture? _____

_____

_____

1. What did you picture for Betsy Ross? _____

_____

2. What did you see for the first American flag? _____

_____

3. What do you see for her taking over her husband's business? _____

_____

4. What did you see for Betsy sewing clothes and flags? _____

_____

2 **Second Paragraph:** The legend says that in 1776 George Washington came to Betsy's home. He asked her to make the new American flag. Together they worked on a design with stars and stripes. He wanted the stars to have six points, but Ross disagreed. She quickly showed him an easy way to make perfect stars with five points. Washington then agreed and the woman went to work.

What did those words make you picture?_____

_____

1. What did you picture for George Washington?_____

_____

2. What did you see for him going to Betsy's home?_____

_____

3. What did you picture for them working together on a design?_____

_____

4. What did you picture for the star Betsy wanted?_____

_____

3 **Third Paragraph:** Ross made a flag with 13 red and white stripes. In the corner was a blue square with a circle of 13 white stars in the middle. This flag is now known as the Betsy Ross flag. It became the official American flag in 1777.

What did those words make you picture?_____

_____

1. What did you picture for Betsy's first flag?_____

_____

2. What colors did you see for the 13 stripes?_____

_____

3. Where did you picture the blue square?_____

_____

4. How did you picture the flag becoming "official"?_____

_____

Critical Thinking

Picture Summary:

Number these in order.

[ ] George Washington asked Betsy Ross to make the new American flag and they worked on a design with stars and stripes.

[ ] Betsy Ross was a young widow who worked as a seamstress making flags and clothes.

[ ] The Betsy Ross flag had 13 red and white stripes and a blue square with a circle of 13 white stars in the middle.

Main Idea:

Check the box that best describes all your images—the main idea.

[ ] Betsy Ross quickly showed Washington an easy way to make stars with five points.

[ ] Betsy Ross was a young widow when she took over her husband's sewing business.

[ ] Betsy Ross was a young seamstress whom many believed made the first American flag.

HOT Questions:

1. What might be a reason why Betsy Ross took over her husband's sewing business?_____

_____

2. Why do you think Washington chose Betsy to sew the first American flag?_____

_____

3. Why do you think Betsy agreed to make the first flag?_____

_____

4. Why would a seamstress be a good person to make the first flag?_____

_____

5. What might be a reason that Betsy wanted to make stars with five points?_____

_____

6. How do you think the fact that we had 13 colonies affected what Betsy put on the flag?_____

_____

Write a Word Summary about <u>Betsy Ross</u>.

_____

_____

_____

_____

_____

_____

_____

_____

_____

_____

_____

_____

_____

_____

Did you use all of the Structure Words? Check each one you used.

☐ What ☐ Size ☐ Color ☐ Number ☐ Shape ☐ Where
☐ Movement ☐ Mood ☐ Background ☐ Perspective ☐ When ☐ Sound

24 London Bridge, AZ.

London Bridge, one of London's famous bridges, now stands in Arizona instead of London. Over 170 years ago, the bridge was built across the river Thames. This bridge was very strong and built of stone. But in 1962, it was discovered that the stone bridge was sinking into the river. Instead of destroying it, the British government sold it.

Stone by stone the bridge was taken apart. The workers put a code on each stone. Then they made a chart so that each stone could be put in the right place when the bridge was eventually put back together. The stones were then put on a boat and shipped to California.

When the ship reached its port, the stones were put on trucks. Then they were driven to their new home. At last, workers put the bridge back together again using the code. The London Bridge now stands in Lake Havasu, Arizona, where over a million people visit it each year.

Vocabulary:

London Bridge: a bridge that was moved from London, England to Arizona
Arizona: a state in the southwest part of the United States
Thames: a river that runs through London
British: from Great Britain

---

1 **First Paragraph:** London Bridge, one of London's famous bridges, now stands in Arizona instead of London. Over 170 years ago, the bridge was built across the river Thames. This bridge was very strong and built of stone. But in 1962, it was discovered that the stone bridge was sinking into the river. Instead of destroying it, the British government sold it.

What did those words make you picture? _____

_____

1. What did you picture for the famous London Bridge? _____

_____

2. What did you picture for it being built of stone? _____

_____

3. How did you see it sinking into the river Thames? _____

_____

4. What did you picture for the British government selling it? _____

_____

2 **Second Paragraph:** Stone by stone the bridge was taken apart. The workers put a code on each stone. Then they made a chart so that each stone could be put in the right place when the bridge was eventually put back together. The stones were then put on a boat and shipped to California.

What did those words make you picture?_____

_____

1. What did you picture for the bridge being taken apart stone by stone?_____

_____

2. How did you see the workers putting a code on each stone?_____

_____

3. What did you picture for the code?_____

_____

4. What did you see for the stones being shipped to California?_____

_____

3 **Third Paragraph:** When the ship reached its port, the stones were put on trucks. Then they were driven to their new home. At last, workers put the bridge back together again using the code. The London Bridge now stands in Lake Havasu, Arizona, where over a million people visit it each year.

What did those words make you picture?_____

_____

1. What did you picture for the stones being put on a truck?_____

_____

2. What color was the truck you pictured?_____

_____

3. What did you see for the bridge being put back together?_____

_____

4. What did you picture for the workers using the code on each stone?_____

_____

Critical Thinking

Picture Summary:

Number these in order.

___ London Bridge was trucked to Arizona and put back together again.

___ London Bridge was falling into the river, so the British government sold it.

___ London Bridge was taken apart stone by stone, coded, and shipped on a boat to California.

HOT Questions:

1. Why do you think the bridge was built of stone?_____

_____

2. Why do you think it was important to have a strong bridge across the river in the city of London?_____

_____

3. What might be a reason for this bridge to start sinking into the river?_____

_____

4. Why do you think the British government sold it instead of destroying it?_____

_____

5. Why do you think the bridge was taken apart before it was moved?_____

_____

6. Why do you think it was important for a code to be put on each stone?_____

Main Idea:

Check the box that best describes all your images—the main idea.

☐ The workers put a code on each stone of the London Bridge so each one could be put back in the right place.

☐ In 1962, it was discovered that the London Bridge was sinking into the river.

☐ London Bridge is a stone bridge that was moved from its original home in London to its new home in Arizona.

Write a Word Summary about <u>London Bridge, AZ</u>.

_____

_____

_____

_____

_____

_____

_____

_____

_____

_____

_____

_____

_____

_____

Did you use all of the Structure Words? Check each one you used.

☐ What	☐ Size	☐ Color	☐ Number	☐ Shape	☐ Where
☐ Movement	☐ Mood	☐ Background	☐ Perspective	☐ When	☐ Sound

Notes:

Analysis of Student Performance:

_____

_____

_____

_____

_____

_____

_____

_____

_____

_____

_____

_____

_____

_____

Visualizing and Verbalizing® Graded Workbooks Color Coding

The colored checkers along the book's spine represent the grade level of the workbook. For example, the four red checkers indicate that the workbook is written at a fourth grade reading level. The colored star helps differentiate between books a, b, and c in each workbook set.